Elizabeth in Paris

What People Are Saying About *Elizabeth in Paris*

"Captivating! My grandchildren thought they were there with Elizabeth, enjoying her adventures in Paris with her mom. They loved the drawings and can't wait to see what she does next. They'll follow her wherever she goes."
— Jean Hall, Grandmother and poet, London

"An absolutely amazing book. It creates strong images in the reader's mind, following everything that Elizabeth is doing. The reader is welcomed into Elizabeth's world, telling us about her favorite things, especially eating ice cream and where she likes to go.

My favorite part is when Elizabeth is describing the fireworks and I can almost see them shooting up in the air, making wonderful patterns.

I really enjoyed this book and I definitely think that Elizabeth's adventures will find a permanent place on my bookshelf."
— Camille Torossian, age 11

The Elizabeth Books

A Day at PreSchool
A Fun Place to Play with New Friends
A picture book to read to kids entering preschool

Elizabeth at School
A Safe Place to Learn
A picture book for ages 6 – 8

Elizabeth in Paris
Traveling with My Mom, the Artist
A picture book for ages 6 – 8

The Flood
The Dangerous Exploits of Three Girls, a Cat and a Boat
A chapter book for ages 9 – 12

Elizabeth in Paris

Traveling with My Mom, the Artist

Written and Illustrated by
Wendy Bartlett

Wendy Bartlett
(2013)

Kensington Hill Books
Berkeley, California

Kensington Hill Books
Berkeley, California

kensingtonhillbooks.com

Ordering Information:
Quantity sales. Special discounts are available on quantity purchases by schools, associations, and others. For details, contact the publisher via the Contact page on the above website.

Elizabeth in Paris: Traveling with My Mom, the Artist /
Wendy Bartlett —1st ed.
ISBN 978-1-9449070-6-8 print
ISBN 978-1-9449070-7-5 ebook

Dedicated to my daughter,
Elizabeth Stark

Elizabeth in Paris
by
Wendy Bartlett

centre Beaubourg
Pompidou Paris

I went to Paris, France this summer with my mother. I got lots of ice cream there because my mother wanted to draw pictures of me, and it's the only way my mother thought I would sit still.

Roof of Galeries Lafayette
15 Juillet 97

My favorite place in Paris is a huge park called Les Tuilleries. It is my favorite because there are lots of things for children to do there. I got to go on the little merry-go-round seven times. Mother says it is probably the last time I can go on it because I will be too old by the time I go to Paris again. She says she understands about how much fun it is. So after every ride, I go after her for more money, and say, "You understand, don't you, Mommy?" And she gives me money for another ride. Also, she is drawing a picture of me, and it takes a long time, thank goodness.

The best part of that merry-go-round ride is trying to put a stick through the rings and collect as many as I can during one ride. Sometimes rings slide off my stick and onto the ground. Mom stops drawing

Les Tuilleries Juillet 15, 77

then, and picks them up for me. The trees
nearby are called Horse Chestnut trees.
Horses on the merry-go-round, get it?

There are other rides in the park, too.
I take the donkey ride. There is a man
and woman there trying to organize their
stubborn donkeys. They are arguing in
French about where the donkeys should
walk, I think. I sit on one for a long time
before they decide. And off we go down
the path. The donkey has long ears,
that's how you can tell he's a donkey
and not a horse.

We just happened to be there on the 14th of July, which is their Independence day like ours is the 4th of July. It is called Bastille Day. So Mom walks us – oh! my poor feet – to the Eiffel Tower where there is a bridge. We sit there and watch the fireworks. We see the most beautiful fireworks you ever saw. The colors of blue and green and yellow and red are all over the sky in beautiful patterns. There are songs in French coming from many loudspeakers. Mom says we need to leave before the end so that we will not be crushed in the subway by the crowds.
I get an ice cream there, too, while we wait for the fireworks to begin. I guess mama is bored, so she is drawing a picture of me eating it.

Bastille Day
14 Juillet 77

15

We go to a place called Montmartre.
There are millions of tourists there.
All summer there are lots of artists, too,
all painting and drawing night scenes
of Paris because tourists like to buy them.
Some draw pictures of the tourists.
That is how the artists earn a living.

I am very hungry, but Mom says all the
food up on that hill is too expensive, so
we have hot dogs. I didn't know you could
have hot dogs in France, too!

Hot Dog in Montmartre
15 Juillet 77.

17

Mom buys me a great toy. Even though it is expensive, she knows it will keep me busy the rest of the trip, so it is worth it. You can see the toy. It is made of wood, and it looks like one of the pieces of wood travels down the line of six pieces. It's hard to explain. Not many people want to stand and watch. They just look and walk on. I am talking quite loud in English all the time, but I can't get a crowd together just now. Maybe they only understand French.

Magic Tricks at l'Orangerie
17 Juillet 77

19

We always seem to have lots of bread left over from our breakfast, so we save it to feed to the pigeons. When I get tired of walking, I reach into Mom's big bag that she carries everywhere, and grab some bread to feed to the pigeons.

As I mentioned, we walk everywhere. When I am too tired and make a big fuss, Mom takes a taxi back to the hotel. If I am just a little bit tired, we have to go in the subway. They have machines in the subway where you can put a coin in and buy chewing gum. I don't usually have gum at home, but I persuade Mom to let me get it in Paris.

When we get home, (that is, to the hotel), my favorite place is a little room which has a bidet. It is pronounced BEEDAY and it is in French. Anyway, you're supposed to wash your bootie in it. You sit on it like it was a horse, and it is full of warm soapy water like a tiny bathtub, and you paddle. I make the bidet for Mom every morning and every evening. Best of all though, I like to wash my socks in it.

washing mama's
socks in the bidet
G. Twillet 77

I wash her socks in it, too. It keeps me
very busy, and out of Mom's hair while
she takes a nap.

There is a museum there though it looks to me like they forgot to take the scaffolding down. It is called the Pompidou. It is in Centre Beaubourg. Scaffolding is what they call what they put outside a building for the painters to stand on when they paint the building on the outside.

There's a great ride inside on a huge pretend monster. You go through a tunnel and it's dark and scary and lights are flashing and things jump out and scare you. Mom lets me go on it four times, and at the end I get chocolate candy from a hole in the papier-mâché mountain. I get lots of chocolate. That's the best part of that museum. Of course, they have paintings upstairs for the parents.

They have glass elevators and lots of escalators, which I love. We find a room full of tables and chairs and people where they tell us all about the famous old cafés and bars in France. I find an old-fashion piano called a player piano, or pianola, that plays songs all by itself.

We went on a boat ride on the River Seine.
I am looking at the amazing old houses,
but the boat rocks me and I feel sleepy.
I am tired from walking so much!

Boat on the Seine

Here I am at a café near the famous
university called the Sorbonne.
I had hot chocolate. We just had to sit
down. I have never walked so much
in my life!

The last thing we do in Paris before we take the plane home, is to go up to the top of the Arc de Triomphe which was built by Napoleon between 1806 and 1836. I am just really tired so I spend most of the time yawning. Mom thinks it will be a great picture so I have to yawn a lot of times so she can draw me. People watch me yawn and her draw.

The boulevard below in this drawing is called the Champs-Élysées. If you go to the end you come to that merry-go-round, and further on you can see The Louvre. It's a very famous museum full of old, famous paintings, but it doesn't interest me much.

L'Arc de Triomphe
17 Juillet 77

33

During our trip to Europe we take six plane rides altogether. Mom says we either have to buy shoes, or take those plane rides, so I wear cheap flip-flops for most of the trip and so does she. You can't have everything, can you? Mama keeps looking at the beautiful shoes in Paris, but she knows she can't have everything, either.

I sit next to a man on the plane who does not understand English very well. But he tries.

I get to go into the cockpit on the plane home. They tell me that they have many women pilots in their company who are very good at flying planes. I think I'll be a pilot when I grow up.

Here I am at home again. It's fun to travel, but it's fun to get home again and to go to sleep! Good night!

Asleep
29 June 77

37

Acknowledgements

As always, the first acknowledgement goes to my wonderful daughter, Elizabeth Stark (BookWritingWorld.com), a great writer and teacher who has guided me every step of my journey with her wise feedback. Nanou Matteson, who was once a part of my writers' group and also one of my wonderful teachers, deserves a hearty thanks. My writers' group is, of course, my mainstay and many thanks go to those who used to be in it, and those who remain to this day: Marilynn Rowland, Sarita Berg, Dean Curtis, Ruth Hanham, Doris Fine, Elizabeth Greene, Joyce Scott, Carol Nyhoff, Karen Bird and others. Thanks go to the many friends who helped me feel okay with the drawings, especially my brother, Tom Gilb, who said I was the illustrator I was looking for.

I would like to thank my friends and advisers at the Bay Area Independent Publishers Association, especially Lorna Johnson, who did the interior layout, and Val Sherer for general good advice.

Special thanks to Ruth Schwartz for getting this to the final stages and making it real!

I would like to thank and acknowledge all the people who run The San Francisco Writers Conference, and, in particular, Michael Larsen, Elizabeth Pomada, and Laurie McLean, for the many ways they have changed my life as I wrote and volunteered for many years since 2008.

Thanks to all those of you who have read this book and written reviews, the author's gold, especially Leo and Charlie! And to Angie Powers for her amazing author photograph!

About the Author

Wendy Bartlett lived in England for thirteen years where she attended the Maria Grey College of Further Education and received her Teaching Certificate. There she majored in art and education, and then taught for two years at a London primary school. Wendy has a B.A. from U.C. Berkeley  in Art History, and has a California Teaching Credential. She worked as a pre-school teacher at the U.C. Berkeley Childcare Center for five years, and occasionally taught children of all ages in Oakland. She has a daughter, Elizabeth Stark, who is a hero in her series, *The Elizabeth Books,* inspired by Elizabeth's childhood.

kensingtonhillbooks.com

Made in the USA
San Bernardino, CA
23 June 2018